spelling

Shirley Clarke & Barry Silsby

Illustrated by David Farris

Headway · Hodder & Stoughton

BRITISH LIBRARY CATALOGUING-IN-PUBLICATION DATA
Clarke, Shirley
   Headstart: spelling. – (Headstart)
   I. Title   II. Silsby, Barry   III. Series
   372.6

   ISBN 0–340–54458–9
   First published 1991

Designed and typeset by DP Press Ltd, Sevenoaks, Kent
Printed in Hong Kong for the educational publishing division of Hodder & Stoughton Ltd, Mill Road, Dunton Green,
Sevenoaks, Kent by Colorcraft.

The aim of this book is to help your child to become a good speller. It relates to the National Curriculum English Attainment Target 4 (Spelling).

- Learning to spell requires a person to **look carefully**. When an adult is unsure of a spelling, he or she is likely to write the word down to see if it 'looks right'. Looking carefully and remembering patterns of letters in words is the most important thing we need to do to become good spellers.

- Spelling is also **physical**. Much of our spelling when writing is automatic. Good spellers only have trouble if they stop writing in the middle of a word or are writing a word with unusual letter patterns. The best way to help your child with this aspect of spelling is to encourage their handwriting skills. (There is a book about handwriting published in this series.)

- Some spellings can be **sounded out**. Unfortunately, only a minority of words in English are written as they sound. Even words which sound similar are often spelt completely differently. For instance, 'they', 'day', 'weigh', all sound the same but are spelt in a completely different way. Where sounds are most useful is in deciding which letter a word begins with.

Most of the activities in these books are involved with developing your child's ability to look carefully and to recognise common patterns of letters in words. Both words and pictures are used to do this. For most activities where words have been used your child should be able to do the activity whether they can read the words or not.

I spy and Sounds similar are intended to help your child with the beginning sounds of words.

Go away, Dictionary game and Learn to spell the easy way, are specifically designed to help your child to learn spellings. These activities will need more involvement with an adult than the others in the book.

Generally children should only learn spellings which they need (for a piece of writing they are doing), which they will use often and which are not too hard for them.

3

I spy

Look at the picture.

How many things can you find beginning with the sound 'b'?

Now try the sound 's'.

We found 10 of each sound.

Can you find more?

Look at the picture and think of other sounds.

How many things can you find that begin with each one?

Sounds similar

Look at the first picture in each row.

Say the word aloud and listen to the sound it begins with. Now put a circle around the picture which begins with the same sound.

ball

ball   car   bus   jumbo jet

pencil   cat   ruler   pig

witch   whale   book   telephone

tree

table

camera

flower

shoe

dog

glove

shark

egg

egg

bird

elephant

fish

chair

chair

chain

television

rocket

Vowel game

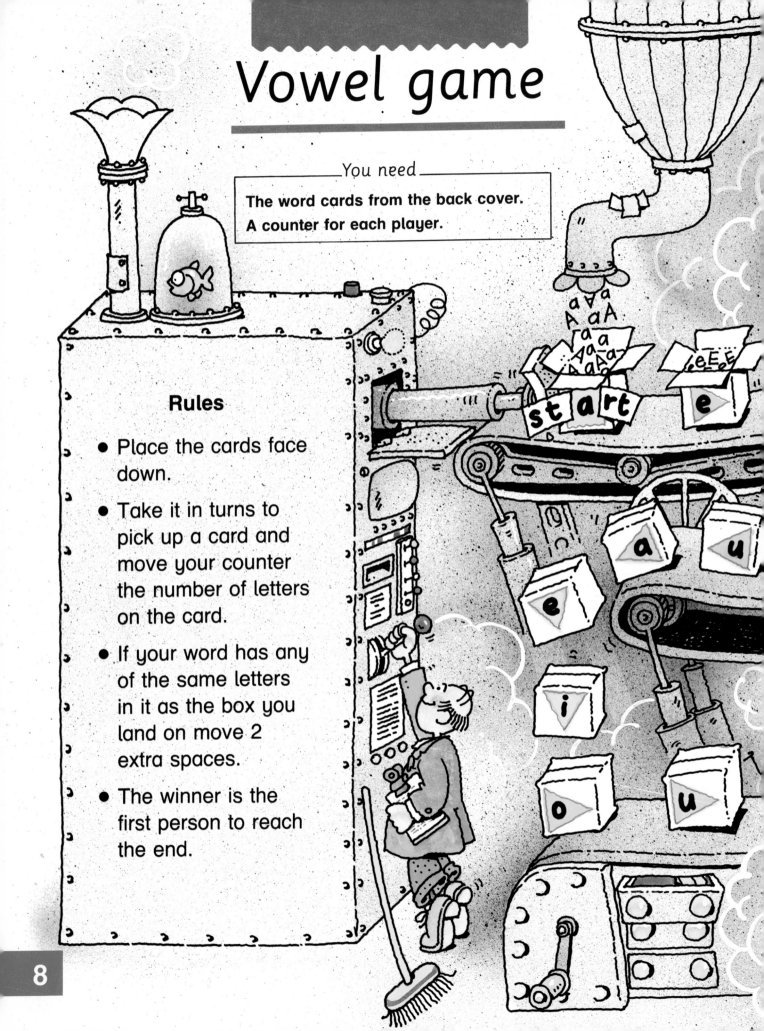

You need

The word cards from the back cover.
A counter for each player.

Rules

- Place the cards face down.

- Take it in turns to pick up a card and move your counter the number of letters on the card.

- If your word has any of the same letters in it as the box you land on move 2 extra spaces.

- The winner is the first person to reach the end.

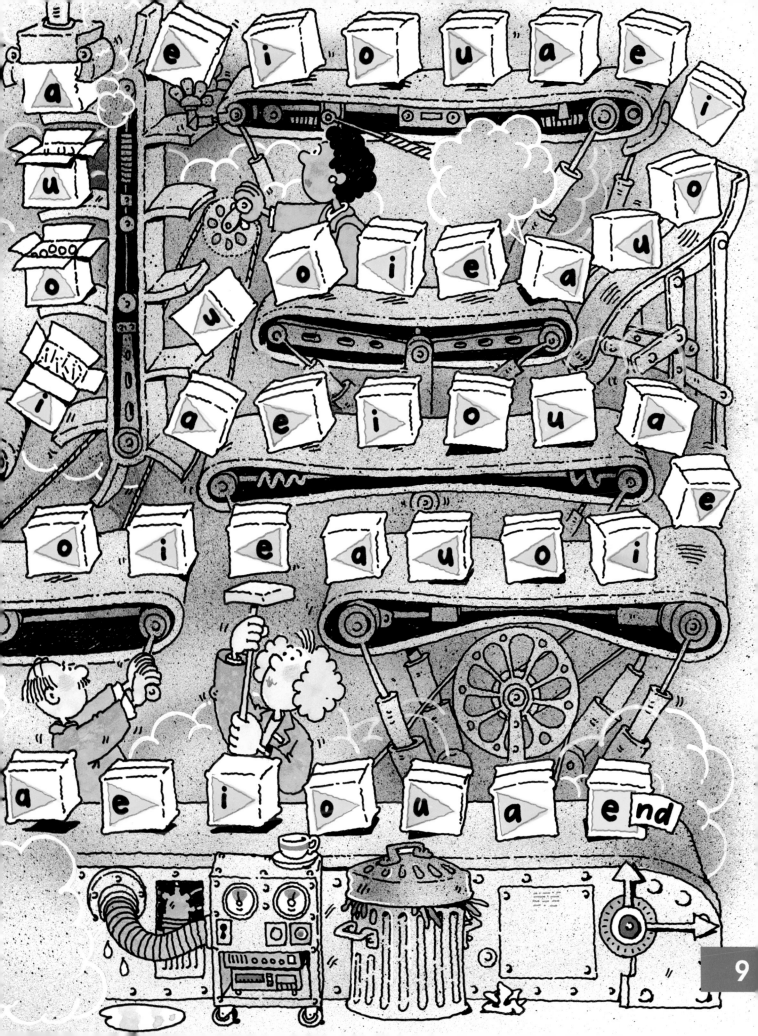

Same as

Look at these animal families.

Only 2 of each family are in the same position.

Put a ring around the 2 which are the same in each family.

Now look at these words.

Put a ring around the 2 words in each row that are the same.

The first row has been done for you.

band	hand	band	land
wring	ring	wrong	wrong
string	sting	sitting	string
bark	dark	park	dark
wired	weird	wired	worried
through	though	thought	through

Word families game

Rules

- Shuffle the cards and put them face down.

- Take it in turns to pick up the top card and put it on the correct family space.

- The player who puts the third card on a family can take all three cards. At the end, when all the cards have been used, the player with the most is the winner.

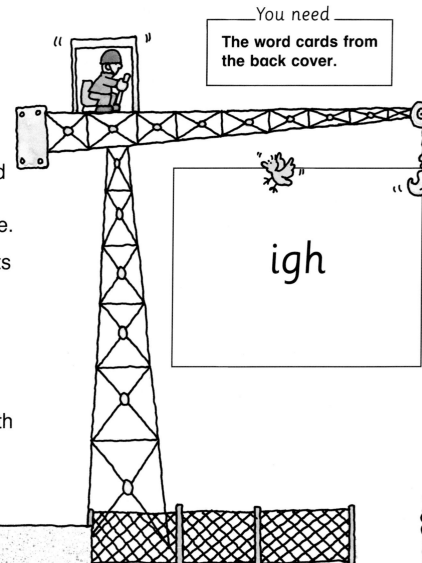

igh

ough

HOSPITAL +

12

and

ion

ing

All the same

Look at the words on the flags.

They all have the word **in** in them.

Put a circle around **in** in each of the words like this:

sting

into

dinner

finish

paint

rain

Now look at the words on the clouds.

Find the word **her** in each of them.

there

other

hero

here

cherry

mother

Which word is in all the words on the balloons?

(Turn the book upside-down to find the answer.)

sandal

band

handle

wand

land

grandad

Go away

This is a game which helps you to learn how to spell words. You will need a pencil, paper and help from an adult or older child.

1 Choose a word you want to spell.

2 Ask an adult or older child to write it down for you.

3 Look carefully at the word. Try to make a picture of it in your mind.

4 Now go away from the word thinking of it all the time.

16

5 Try to write the word on your own on a different piece of paper.

6 Go back to the word with your piece of paper. Look at what you have got right.

7 How do you need to change yours to get it exactly right?

8 Now go away and try again. This time you should be getting more accurate.

9 Keep doing this until you get the word exactly right.

10 At first you might need lots of goes but with practice you will get quicker and quicker.

Word patterns

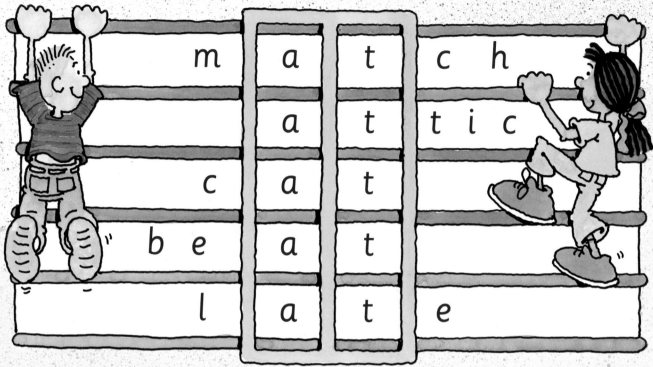

	m	a	t	c	h
	m	a	t	t	i	c
	c	a	t		
be	a	t			
l	a	t	e		

Look carefully at these words.

Can you see the pattern?

Try making these word patterns yourself.

Make sure you get the letters in the right place in the frame.

rent		r	e	n	t	
tender		t	e	n	d	e	r
end			e	n	d	
enough						
broken						

hurt
urgent
fur
pure
curtain

h u r t
u r g e n t

son
only
strong
bone
upon

s o n
o n l y

horse
fork
worse
order
store

h o r s e

19

Dictionary game

When adults don't know how to spell a word they often try it out to see if it 'looks right'.

Then they might look the word up in a dictionary to check it.

A dictionary tells you what a word means and how to spell it.

Look at these words.
Only one on each page is spelt right.
Look at them carefully.
Put a tick against the one you think looks right.

blak

blac

black

mother

mothor

muther

familly

fammily

family

through

throgh

thrugh

gren

green

grene

Now ask an adult to look the words up in a dictionary with you to check them.

fold here

fold here

fold here

fold here

Write word here	First try	Second try

22